Wellington and
Kevin are going to
the pond.

Kevin picks up a stick with string on the end.

Wellington picks up
a stick with a net on
the end.

The dogs go to the
pond to catch a fish.

The dogs sit with
the net and the
string in the water.

Kevin feels a tug on the string. Tug, tug.

Kevin has a frog.
Wellington has a frog.

Wellington and
Kevin let the frogs
go. No fish today!